This book belongs to

....

make believe ideas ltd

The Wilderness, Berkhamsted, Hertfordshire, HP4 2AZ, UK.

www.makebelieveideas.com

Written by Sarah Creese.
Illustrated by Stephanie Thannhauser.

Can you believe that

A DAZZLE of ZEBRAS

is the name for a group of zebras?
Well, ta-da, it is! Look inside
to discover the funny names for
other animal families. Off we go!

Sarah Creese • Stephanie Thannhauser

make
believe
ideas

A family of animals is called a special word:

a **FLOCK** of **SHEEP**,

A FLOCK OF SHEEP

a **PACK** of **WOLVES**

A PACK OF WOLVES

Have you heard of cows?

A HERD OF COWS

or **COWS**, a mooing **HERD**.

Each group has
a different name;
there are many
more to see.
Let's turn the page
to meet them all –
it's showtime now
for…

ME!

ZEBRAS are a DAZZLE
in their showbiz black and whites.

A DAZZLE
OF ZEBRAS

PORCUPINES are a **PRICKLE**— but they're perfectly polite.

ELEPHANTS blow their trumpets in a trunk-to-tail **PARADE.**

A BASK OF CROCODILES

CROCODILES are a BASK,

GORILLAS are a noisy BAND

and RHINOS
make a
CRASH!

BATS fly in a CAULDRON,

A CAULDRON OF BATS

making potions fizz and flash.

PENGUINS are a PARCEL,
neatly tied up with a bow.

A TOWER OF GIRAFFES

GIRAFFES stand in a TOWER, teetering up from hoof to head.

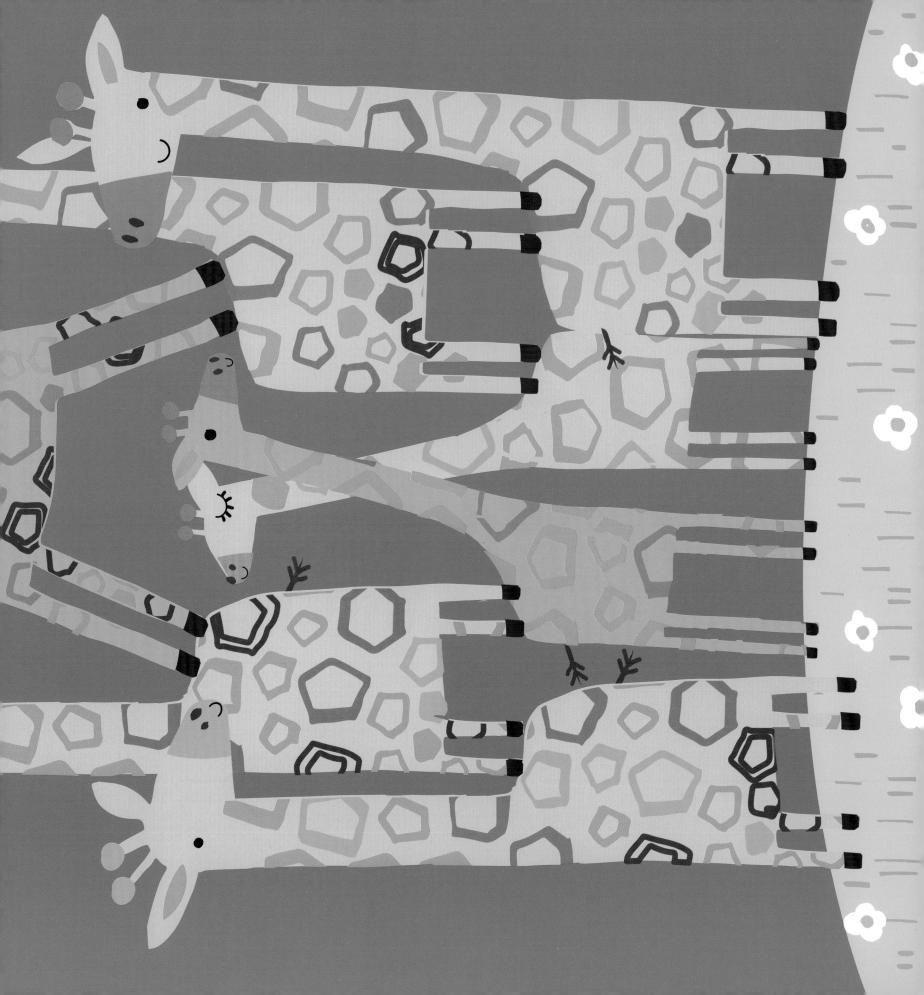

TOADS prefer to tie up in a slimy **KNOT** instead.

A KNOT OF TOADS

A BUSINESS OF FLIES

HIGH-FLYERS OF THE MONTH

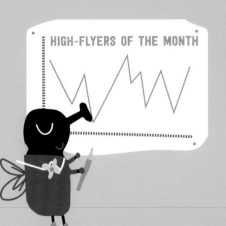

FLIES become a **BUSINESS**, doing jobs for all the bugs.

FLYING TIPS

The world is full
of **ANIMALS**.
How many can you see?

Now, choose the **GROUP** you like the best.

Which **ONE** will it be?